MW00605462

*Put Your F***ing Phone Away!*

A STORYBOOK FOR ADULTS

WRITTEN BY THOMAS MON

ILLUSTRATED BY TRINH BANKS

HTTP://PYFPABOOK.COM

© 2016 FORSTLE, LLC   PRINTED IN PRC   ISBN 978-0-9975360-0-3

Alarm Cluck

Your eyes still heavy from the weight of the night.
The sun shining in your bedroom blinds your sight.
Tap, tap, swipe from the coziness of your sheets.
You love your phone; it has seven texts, four tweets.
You want to stay in bed all day!
Instead, you hear your mother say...

*"Get out of bed! Put your f***ing phone away."*

Cracked Shell

It's time to brush and rinse to make your shell shine.
"Ding" goes your phone, your friends start to come online.
Brushing with one hand, texting with the other.
Viral news abounds, so much to discover!
Click-bait social media—can't look away.
Staring at your phone when you hear your mom say...

"Stop reading that junk! Put your f***ing phone away."

Egg-scuse Me!

Win one more battle before going downstairs.
Post an epic screenshot in hopes of more shares.
Although friends posted theirs, only yours got liked.
"Ding!" An invite from Arnold: "Try Global Strike!"
Someone's at the door, but you want to play.
Too bad, you can't, then you hear your mom say...

"I'm not going to say it again! Put your f***ing phone away."

Sunny Side Up

Egg Carton Level 9 is almost complete.
Your stomach growls, telling you it's time to eat.
You check your inbox, only to find more SPAM.
No, I'm not lonely tonight, go away Ma'am!
Dad reads the encouraging words of the day.
Then breaking the silence, you hear your mom say...

*"Help me find Ellie!! Put your f***ing phones away."*

Loading the Carton

Quickly grab your backpack, don't forget your lunch.
Google, play Marky Mark and the Funky Bunch.
With your ear buds on, you skip to the bus stop.
Mom snaps a photo, catching you as you hop.
Your music makes other noises go away.
And so you're unable to hear your mom say...

"I love you! Please just put your f***ing phone away."

Egg-Roll Call

In the hall before class, you see all your friends.
View the latest tweets influencing the trends.
You have five minutes for posting them dank memes.
A selfie with Amie, the egg of your dreams.
Your ringtone plays too loudly; it's not your day.
Because that's right when you hear your teacher say...

*"Phones are not allowed in school! Put that f***ing phone away."*

Chicken Seizer

While you're at school, your parents go grab a bite.
Check for a coupon on the Boiling Pot site.
One table over, some dude photos their dish.
At another table, some Gefilte fish.
Dad cannot find a discount, to his dismay,
Abruptly interrupted, he hears mom say...

*"Oh, forget it! I'm hungry, let's eat! Put your f***ing phone away."*

Free Range

MOM AND ELLIE SPEND THE DAY AT PERDEW PARK.
MOM ALWAYS NEEDS HER CAFFEINE—SHE LIKES IT DARK.
ELLIE'S PUT IN THE SANDBOX, MOM FINDS A BENCH.
ELLIE LOVES THE SAND, BUT THIS BOX HAS A STENCH!
MOM'S ALWAYS ON HER PHONE, IT'S NOT A FUN DAY.
IF ONLY ELLIE COULD TALK, SHE'D WANT TO SAY...

"Why don't you ever play with me?
*Put your f***ing phone away."*

Eggs-it the Bus

School day's over, bus "E" stops at your street.
Like drones we exit, our smartphones drop the beat.
All heads down, music and games in full throttle.
No plans to meet later — no spin the bottle.
Not enough power for the rest of the day,
You need to charge it, but you hear your mom say...

*"You're so addicted to that thing! Put your f***ing phone away."*

Chicken of the C+

Drag your books up the stairs, it's time to work.
Twenty chapter maps to write, you give a smirk.
Your music is playing; your mind is at ease.
A sudden knock at the door; you almost wheeze.
Hiding your phone, you hope the knock goes away.
You have no such luck as you hear your dad say...

*"Do your homework! Put your f***ing phone away."*

Deviled Eggs

Only a minute left, the game is now tied.
The coach puts you in hoping to turn the tide.
The ball is kicked through the air, where will it land?
Dad misses the ball passing the goalie's hand.
The Poachers have scored! The sideline cheers "Hurray!"
Dad looks up, knowing what mom's about to say...

*"What the hell are you doing?! Put your f***ing phone away."*

The Eggmaster

Celebrating the win, your friends come over.
The Eggsbox turns on, each grabs a controller.
As the first game ends, the phones start to awaken.
Faces in screens, all signs of life have been taken.
Mom looks around the room, face full of dismay.
She clears her throat loudly and you hear her say...

*"Why don't you kids talk anymore? Put your f***ing phones away."*

Eggs Benedict

Together at the table, ready to eat.
Baby Ellie's in her seat, not by our feet.
Dad catches the news, while you text a friend back.
This silence at dinner sets your mom aback.
For a moment she thinks, "Have we lost our way?"
With her own phone in hand, no one's left to say...

*"How was your day? Put your f***ing phone away."*

INTEGGRITY
WISDOM IS KNOWING
WHICH PATH TO TAKE.
INTEGGRITY IS TAKING IT.

Re-COOP-erating

The night comes quickly; under the blanket you hide.
Although you said goodnight to mom — yeah, you lied.
With phone close to your face and volume set low.
Private browsing enabled, time for a show.
An ominous creek of the door halts your play.
You suddenly freeze, as you hear your mom say...

"Do you want me to break that f***ing thing?

Put your f***ing phone away."

Fried Eggs

It's late at night and the kids are asleep.
What a day it has been, mom and dad are beat.
Both on the couch, yet they are so far apart.
Divided by phones, conversations can't start.
The TV stays on with shows on auto-play.
Why is it like this? Why is this every day?

*"Maybe we all should just put our f***ing phones away."*